MW00585429

MAILBOX MONEY

*A Salesman's Journey
to Learn the Secrets
of Business and Life*

Joe Ferrer

MAILBOX MONEY
Copyright © 2018 Joe Ferrer
All Rights Reserved

This book or any portion thereof may not be reproduced or used in any manner
whatsoever without the express written permission of the publisher except in
the case of reprints in the context of reviews, quotes, or references.

Printed in the United States of America
ISBN: 978-0-9974608-2-7
Library of Congress Control Number: 2018965039

Published by Cocoon to Wings Publishing
Wesley Chapel, Florida 33545
www.StephanieOutten.com
(813) 906-WING

Cover design by Ereka Thomas Designs

Limit of Liability/Disclaimer of Warranty. While the publisher and author have used their best efforts in
preparing this book, they make no representation or warranties with respect to the accuracy or complete-
ness of the contents of this book. (The author and/or publisher do not guarantee that anyone following
these strategies, suggestions, ideas, will be successful. The advice and strategies contained herein may
not be suitable for your situation. You should consult with a professional where appropriate. Neither
the publisher nor author shall be liable for any loss of profit or any other commercial damage including,
but not limited to, special, incidental, consequential, or other damages.)

TABLE OF CONTENTS

THE DISCIPLINES

ACKNOWLEDGEMENTS

....

FIRST AND FOREMOST, I want to give honor and glory to God. Thank you for the personal journey that I am on, all that I have learned and will learn along the way. To my wife, Minerva Ferrer, I thank you for being you. You make me better each and every day, and I thank you. You continue to push me to not settle and to expect greatness.

To my kids - Anthony, Yaznay, Noah, and Irish - you are what motivates me, and I hope I can inspire you to be the best version of yourself. To my countless family members and friends, I thank you for your tremendous prayers and support.

To my publisher, Stephanie Outten of Cocoon to Wings Publishing, thanks so much for bringing this to life. Words cannot express my gratitude for you and the care and love you had on this project.

To my editor, E. Claudette Freeman of E. Claudette Freeman Literary Services, my graphic designer, Ereka Thomas of Ereka Thomas Designs, and my proofreader, Tracy L. Carter of Sista Girl Publications - THANK YOU! Your partnership with me and Stephanie made the Mailbox Money vision a reality. You all are an amazing team!

Last, but not least, I want to give a special shout out to the person reading this book. Yeah, you! The one with the book in your hand, reading it on a device, or listening to it on audio. Without you taking the time to read this book, it would just sit on the shelf. By you reading this book, you are taking the journey and bringing Mailbox Money to life. I hope the principles and the four disciplines in this book have an amazing effect on your business and the people you most care for. From the bottom of my heart I THANK YOU! Now, enough with the mushy stuff. Let's start the journey!

"Mailbox Money is a great read! It speaks to the power of leveraging your resources. It helps you understand that you can be in business for yourself, but you are never by yourself."

ESZYLFIE TAYLOR
President and founder of Taylor Insurance and Financial Services

"Combining unique story telling and business motivation is no easy feat. Even harder to do well. Mailbox Money pulls it off."

TREVOR PRICE
Principal Outlook Company and Former All Pro Professional Football Player

. . . .

CHAPTER 1

Intro

A SALESMAN ARRIVED AT the office mid-morning, much later than his colleagues. He walked in slowly listening to music through his headphones. He drank his coffee, spoke to a couple of friends, and finally made his way into his office. His office was plain, no décor - just an old computer on the desk with a couple papers scattered around. While sitting in his office, with no one to call, the salesman wondered what was the key to success and how he could become really good at what he did. He was tired of struggling to be barely average as he looked at the sales reports and consistently saw his name at the bottom of the list.

He sat back and began to think of who he could ask about the key to success. He got up from his desk and walked down the hallway to one of the most successful people in the office. This woman had a thriving business and had acquired many clients throughout the years. Those clients regularly came to the office to see her. No matter what part of town she visited, people knew her. She was confident and had been with the company for a long time, so if anyone knew the key to success surely it would be her.

Her door was cracked, and the light was on. He knocked softly and waited to see if she would allow him in.

"Come in," her voice rang through the door.

"Good morning! I have a question, but I'm a little nervous to ask." The salesman wrung his hands together with hesitant anxiety.

"No time to be nervous. What is your question?" The woman stared at the salesman willing him to spit it out.

"What can I do to be just like you?" He took a breath and hastily continued. "I want clients like you. I want awards like you have. I want your lifestyle. I want you to be my mentor. Would you mind just telling me the key to your success?" The salesman stopped talking to allow the mentor to respond.

She laughed saying, "Everyone that works here asks the same thing. Not a week goes by that someone isn't knocking on that door asking me the key to my success. Everyone wants to know what my secret is." She sat back in her chair and waited for his next question. She knew what it would be because it was the same question she got from other salesmen who had come to see her in the past.

As if on cue, the salesman laid out his questions, "Tell me, please! What is it? What can I do? I'm tired of being barely average."

For some odd reason, the woman liked the salesman's energy and spirit and was willing to make the investment in him. She leaned across her desk and said, "If you show up to this office at seven thirty in the morning every day and work a full day for the next two months straight, I will mentor you and I will tell you the key."

The salesman pondered for a minute. He already struggled to get into the office by ten o'clock in the morning, so seven thirty would be tough. "Seven thirty? That's pretty early. Can we do eight thirty instead?"

She got up from her desk, walked out into the hallway as she laughed at the salesman's request. The salesman went running after her saying," l will be here. I promise!"

"Do not tell anyone about our deal, and do not even speak to me until after you have done as I asked," the mentor was adamant. "I need to know first and foremost that you are disciplined. Trust me, I will not share the key with you if you cannot at least show up."

Two months later the salesman showed up and excitedly knocked on his mentor's door.

"Today marks two months." His smile was full. "Getting here early every day helped me learn so much. I took the time to study all the products and sales material. Now will you tell me the key to your success?"

The mentor looked up at the salesman. She couldn't help but smile. "Good job! I knew I liked you for a reason." She waved him to take a seat before asking, "Have you ever heard of mailbox money and the legend of the golden mailbox?"

The salesman smirked with irritation. "What are you talking about? A *golden mailbox?* What is this *mailbox money* foolishness?" His voice grew animated. "I want to know what *you* do and what products you sell. Tell me where you buy your leads from. I did my part, now you do yours. Give me the key to success."

The mentor sat back, folding her arms across her chest. She chuckled at the salesman, finding humor in his reaction. "If you think it is something, like a line that I say, or something as simple as that, then everyone would say it." She continued to laugh, but the salesman didn't find it funny.

"Okay tell me about this golden mailbox or mailbox money as you call it." He put his elbows on her desk, clasping his hands together.

"Are you sure you're ready to learn the secret?" She paused for his response. Not getting one, she continued. "Some people say they are ready, but they really are not," she looked him in the eyes.

"You better believe I'm ready! I've been waiting for this for two months." The salesman rubbed his hands together, sure he was about to receive the answers he'd been waiting on.

"Do you have your passport?" She looked at him.

"Yes, I do!"

She smiled at him and said, "I'm not just going to tell you about the golden mailbox, I'm actually going to take you on a journey to discover it. Pack your bags, salesman. You and I are going on a trip. Be ready to leave Monday at seven thirty in the morning. Meet me at the airport."

The salesman got excited. He knew this was it - the break he was looking for. His mentor was going to take him to the golden mailbox - the place where she learned everything, so she could teach him the secret to her success.

CHAPTER 2

Journey to the Golden Mailbox

THE SALESMAN ARRIVED AT the airport and found his mentor waiting for him.

"Good morning!" It was so early, yet the mentor was super chipper.

Without even a 'good morning,' the salesman jumped right in with his standard question. "Okay, I'm here," he yawned through his words. "What is mailbox money and the legendary Kung Fu golden mailbox stuff? How does it work? Where do I buy it?"

She couldn't help but laugh at the young salesman as he continued blurting out his silly questions. "Be easy young man. In no time you *will* understand what this is all about." She patted him on the shoulder as they boarded the plane. After taking their seats, she said, "Take this short journey with me. Prior to our final destination to the golden mailbox, we must make a few critically important stops."

"You keep saying *mailbox money* and *the golden mailbox*. Which is it? Are they two different things in two different places?" Confusion laced his face.

"They are the same. The golden mailbox is where the mailbox money comes from." The mentor smiled as she patiently awaited his next set of questions.

"I'm starting to think you're talking in riddles. Why are we making these stops? Why can't we just go straight to the golden mailbox?" He shifted in his seat with agitation.

"You must learn the four disciplines on these stops in order to take the easier path to the golden mailbox," said the mentor. "If we do not make these stops, we may get there at some point, but the long way to the mailbox is dangerous and risky."

"The *easier path*? *Dangerous and risky*? Wait, where are you taking me?" He got anxious. Stress sweat formed in his armpits. He shook his head. "Could I die on this trip? Especially since this plane is so small. Now, I'm scared!"

The salesman made her day. She wanted to laugh but didn't want to make him feel bad. Instead, she spoke to him with ease, "Do you mind if we make these brief stops to learn the disciplines? These disciplines are symbolic of a critical piece of information you must know."

"I don't mind as long as you get me there safely!"

"As you gain understanding in one place, we can then continue on to the next stop. There are four stops in total before we finally arrive to the golden mailbox," she held up four fingers. "If I do not think you learned the discipline, the pilot may be forced to take you on the dangerous path to the mailbox. Trust me, you don't want that! Many people don't return, and we don't want that to be you." The way she gently spoke to him showed her concern. "I want you to come home and bring others to the golden mailbox. But, you first must go alone with me. So, let us stay on course and make sure we arrive where we need to. As she clicked her seatbelt, she looked at him and continued, "Buckle your seatbelt and open your mind as we take off."

CHAPTER 3

Mountain Views

AFTER A LONG, TURBULENT flight, the plane landed on a landing strip on top of the mountain. It didn't seem like a lot of planes landed there often as weeds were everywhere amongst the grass. The salesman complained the whole flight. He talked about how old the plane was and asked the pilot if it had its maintenance papers. Upon arrival, the salesman, having no clue where they were, asked, "Mentor, where in the world are we? That was the scariest plane ride ever. I thought for sure you said we were not going the dangerous way."

"The flight was a little rough but, trust me, this was not the long path. We are just getting started. Grab your backpack and let's go."

As they walked, the salesman ate the last apple he had from the plane. He threw the half-eaten apple over the side of the mountain.

The mentor was dumbfounded. "Why did you throw that away?

"It's just an apple. Some birds will eat it."

By that point they had gotten further and further away from the plane, to the point where they could no longer see it when they looked back. They walked deeper into the forest and got to the side of the mountain. As they walked alongside the mountain, the salesman looked amazed at how tall and wide the trees were. He noticed one of the trees looked different than the others. "Mentor, what's wrong with this tree? It looks so different."

"Yes! That is the tree the Indians called 'Mama Earth.' So sad! This tree was one of the oldest trees ever recorded. People from all over the world would come here to see it. Unfortunately, the local authorities were treating the forest with chemicals, and a large amount of that chemical spilled at the base of the tree."

He was dumbfounded. "They couldn't' fix it? There has to be something they could have done."

"Sadly, there is nothing that can be done now. Within weeks this tree that people loved, died and became discolored. This tree will soon fall, and when it does, many who knew it in its full beauty will mourn. This tree means a lot to me." She stood in silence as she looked at the tree. She hugged and kissed the tree before they continued their walk in the forest.

Along the walk, the mentor asked the salesman about his

life and his struggles in the business. They talked for hours getting deeper and deeper into the journey.

"Salesman tell me more about what urged you to come see me. It seemed pretty serious when you came into the office that morning," she stopped to look at him.

"There is so much. I just do not feel I'm doing the best I can. I don't feel connected to my clients or enjoy my business that much. I've heard that work is supposed to be fun and enjoyable, but I am just not having the fun I thought I would have. Maybe if I was doing better, things might be better," he said.

"Work can be fun, but most importantly it is work. Even someone that enjoys what they do, if they want to be great, they have to prepare and work harder than their peers. There will be good days and challenging days even for the most successful people. Your connection with your clients is an important concern. No clients mean no business, so find a way to connect with the clients you have. Let me ask you a question. How long have you felt like this? This feeling of wanting to do better and wanting success," she questioned.

"These feelings are pretty new. I have been frustrated with so much. I look at the people in the office that are close to my age and I want to be successful like them. I want to be like them right now. I don't want to wait. I want to be on top. Every time I see the numbers it frustrates me seeing my peers outperform me. I just can't seem to see myself as being successful in this industry. I need to know this secret, so I can be like them as fast as possible. Hopefully this mailbox money thing you're going to tell me about will help me to get there."

"Are you sure you have prepared yourself and studied the necessary information related to your job?" She asked.

"I read books. I study all the time. I feel like I may know too much for my own good sometimes. My friends are going out at night while I am the one that is reading and trying to better myself. For whatever reason, it is not benefitting me at all and I am consistently below average." His voice cracked.

The mentor interjected. "Feeling like you know too much can be frustrating. I had similar struggles before I went on my journey with my teacher. I was a mess. My boss actually told me that if my numbers did not get better they would fire me. My journey to the golden mailbox was a matter of me keeping my job. I had a family, so I had to do something. I was transformed when I returned, and I have continued to grow my business. I not only have to study, but I must apply everything I learned. This is what I hope will happen for you. Not everyone that has gone on the journey comes back with success stories."

The salesman, unconvinced by what she was saying, had a look of disbelief on his face. He did not believe his mentor had ever gone through the things she shared with him. She was too successful to have struggled like him.

The salesman noticed night was falling and asked, "What are we really doing out here? What does this walk in the mountains have to do with anything? He needed to learn how to take a breath. Clearly that was foreign to him because he never stopped with the questions. "Who are we going to see, and how on earth could they be successful here? There aren't any people here."

She laughed. Much of her time had been spent doing that since they started this journey. In her Spanish accent, she said, "Ay dios mio." She stopped. "Here is the perfect spot."

The salesman looked around perplexed. "Where is the hotel? What are we going to do for food and sleep?"

"I'm going to get some sleep now. We have a long day tomorrow."

The salesman was totally confused having no clue why he - a city boy - was there in the middle of the forest. He hadn't even realized the mentor had been carrying tents in the bag on her shoulder. They set up their tents under a gorgeous sky where they could see stars, and there they slept. When morning came, the mentor told the salesman, "I found us water and filled it up in these filtered thermoses."

The salesman, dying of thirst, said, "Thank you so much." He drank down half of it before the mentor tried to stop him.

"Slow down! It took me a while to get that water." She reached for the thermos but was too late.

The salesman drank the rest of the water. *Buuuuuuuuuuuurrrrrrrrrrrp.* Whew! That was the best water I've had in my whole life." He packed up his tent.

The mentor, still in shock from how loud the salesman

belched, said, "You're just like everyone else. That water might be your last." She packed up her tent and belongings. "Let's go!"

They began to walk and really take notice of how beautiful the landscape was.

"Thanks for bringing me," the salesman smiled. "I've never seen anything like this in my life. Are you bringing me here just to show me the beauty and what rich people can do?" He asked.

She burst out laughing again. "So, you think I'm here to sleep in the woods for fun? I'm here for you." She pointed toward him.

The salesman, not knowing if he should believe her, continued to walk and appreciate the view. He noticeably walked slowly and looked exhausted. "I'm so hungry and thirsty. Can I get some of your water?" he begged of his mentor as he wiped the corners of his dry mouth.

She looked at him. "I've been waiting for you to ask me that."

"Well, can I have some?" He impatiently asked.

"No, you cannot! But, what you *can* do is walk one and a half miles in that direction," she pointed toward the trees, "and you will come to a river. Take water from there and fill it in this special thermos, and it will filter it for you," said the mentor. She sat down by a tree and began reading a book. "It should take you two hours to go and come back. I'll see you later. Be careful!"

The thirsty salesman knew he had no choice but to go. While walking, he heard something running in the distance. Scared, he covered himself with leaves and laid still for several minutes. What he saw, peeking from his hiding spot, was a wild pack of ferocious wolves in the distance running from something. The water was only twenty-five yards away. He had to decide if he would fill up the water, wait it out, or run for his life to get back.

He feared the wolves. But he really feared what the wolves were running from. Thirst, taking over the salesman, made him run to rapidly fill up his thermos. He heard a loud roar deep in the forest. He stopped filling the thermos and began to sprint back to the campsite. As he ran, he felt as if he was being chased. He looked back and didn't see anything. Every time he stopped for air, he looked back in fear of what he thought was coming after him. He didn't see anything. *Is something really out there? Am I looking for something that wasn't even real?* He asked himself as he continued running for his life and back to the safety of his mentor.

When he returned to the campsite, the mentor looked up from her book. "I see you found it alright. Why did it take you so long?"

Out of breath and lying on his back, he panted, "You made it sound so easy. I actually saw a small pack of wolves, and something out there was chasing them. I almost didn't get the water." He was exasperated. "Once I did, I got back here as fast as I could. Can't believe I did all that for water."

She stood over him not acknowledging his comments about the wolves and something chasing them. "Well, this time don't drink it all at once. We have some walking to do."

The salesman sat up, shocked she didn't flinch at his comment about the wolves. "No way! This water is going to be sipped like fine wine." He let go of the fear he felt in the woods in order to continue on.

The mentor pointed toward the plants in the forest. "Look! Burdock stalks! Go grab me some please." She looked like she had seen a five-course meal in the plants.

"Grab you some of what? That wild plant over there? What are you going to do with it?" The salesman was bewildered.

"I'm going to eat it. Do you have better options?" She asked him, not waiting for his response. "With no food, you will get very sick up here. If I put the burdock in a fancy can or in the organic vegetable aisle at the store, would you want it then?" She stared at him. "This is as organic as it gets." The mentor ate the burdock. She explained to him the properties of the plant and how it was edible and a good source of food.

"You probably have no clue where half of the foods in the supermarket come from or how they look in their natural environment. You're not alone! We have changed from an agricultural community to a technological people and have not put importance on this. Remember, food does not come from the store; it is only sold there. Take the time to learn more about stuff like this. Next thing you know you will be eating manufactured vegetables and won't even know the difference because you don't know what they should look like. Knowledge is power," she said.

Because he was so hungry, the salesman decided to try it. As he ate it, he licked his fingers. "Not bad! It reminds me a little bit of artichokes. Can't believe someone like you would know about this."

"Why? Because I am a woman or because I have money?" The mentor didn't allow his comment to faze her. "Do not be so shallow, salesman. What you will come to find out is some of the best things in life are free." She chewed on the burdock stalk and drank her water.

As they continued, they came to the side of the mountain where the view was breathtaking. They were so high up it felt like they were in the clouds. They could see villages and animals running down beneath. That was the point they had been trying to make it to.

The mentor inhaled deeply. "At last, here we are! This is the place, just as I remembered it. Look at the beauty. What a perfect day! I would rather be no other place than here with you, young man."

Never one to mince words, the salesman said, "I'm hungry. I slept in the woods and walked two hours for water. I could think of better places to be than here. Then, he smiled. "But I will admit, this view is amazing. It's one I will never forget. It feels like we are just as high up as we were on the plane ride." He looked over at his mentor, saying, "By the way, did you know this was my first time on a small, private plane?"

"Wow! Why didn't you say anything? Were you scared?"

"Of course, I was scared, but I was so focused on the golden mailbox I didn't care." He continued taking in the view. "By the way, where is the golden mailbox? Is it around here somewhere? I'm sure there is something inside of it you want to show me. Or, are we just here to see this amazing view?"

The mentor stared at the salesman as he kept talking. It was surprising she hadn't gotten annoyed with him yet. His impatience may have worn someone else thin.

He paced the floor of the mountain. "Can't believe I flew up here for a view. I'm starving and half dead. You can't be serious. I'm ready to go." Just as he said that, he looked off in the distance and saw a tree full of fruits. Hunger took over. "Is that an apple tree?" He inquired.

"Why, yes, it is! These trees have the best apples ever. The only thing is they must be washed off very well because of the pollen in the air here. You will get very sick if you do not rinse them off with lots of water," she uttered.

The salesman was discouraged. "I only have half my water left."

"Use half of that and rinse it. Save the rest for drinking." The mentor always had a solution.

"So, I can only get one apple?" He seemed surprised.

"That would be my recommendation," his mentor stayed focused on the tree.

The young salesman decided not to go against the mentor.

She had been right thus far, and he was still learning. The young salesman saw the apple tree up close and realized how high up he needed to climb for the apples. He spent close to an hour trying to climb the tree to get two apples - one for him and one for the mentor.

When he finally got up where the fruit hung, the mentor shouted, "Get me that one." She pointed to one on a branch much further than where he was. "It looks perfect."

It took him an extra fifteen minutes to get the apple the mentor requested. Finally, down from the tree, the salesman sat down and washed the apple just as he was instructed. They both sat on the edge of the mountain and enjoyed their apples.

When the mentor looked over, she questioned, "Where is the apple?"

"It's gone!" The salesman licked his lips. "That was the best apple I have ever had in my life."

"Did you eat the core of the apple as well? Hopefully you spit out the seeds. They are poisonous," the mentor looked worried.

"I ate it all. I did spit out the seeds, though. That apple was so good. I would get another, but I don't have water to rinse it off, and I don't want to get sick and end up with the bubble guts." The salesman rubbed his stomach.

"What are *bubble guts*?" The mentor blurted out.

The salesman looked at her, while continuing to rub his stomach until the mentor understood what he meant.

They laughed together before packing up and heading back to the plane.

When the pilot saw them coming toward the plane, he ran to greet them with fruits, nuts, and water. The pilot, from experience, knew they would be hungry and without water. The salesman grabbed the snacks. "Thanks so much. I really appreciate it since I was out of water." He chewed with his mouth open. "I didn't want to say anything, but I did not think I would make it back here. These snacks hit the spot."

The salesman gave the snack bag back to the pilot. When the pilot looked inside, there wasn't a crumb left.

"Wow! You devoured that fast. Where is the core of the apple?" The pilot asked.

"I ate it all. It wasn't as good as the apple we had in the mountains, but it sure was good," said the salesman.

As the pilot started up the engine, the salesman looked at the mentor. "Sorry we didn't find what you were looking for. I did enjoy that view, though. I'm just really happy to be back on this beautiful plane with air conditioning, no bugs biting me.

"What we are looking for will take time. I have confidence we will find it, young man." The plane took off and accelerated into the sky. The salesman sat back and dozed off. The mentor also sat back, but rather than rest, she jotted notes inside her journal.

. . . .

CHAPTER 4

Veeola

THIRTY MINUTES LATER, THE plane landed at a nearby air strip. This air strip was much more official than the one on the mountain. There was a fuel truck and a man that was servicing the planes. The salesman looked and saw a restroom. He jogged to it. When the salesman came back from the bathroom he looked energetic and rejuvenated.

The mentor asked, "Did you have bubble guts?"

"No way! Just got a chance to wash my face and freshen up. Where are we off to now?" His same level of enthusiasm about finding the golden mailbox returned.

"This will be a quick stop. We have to see an old friend of mine named Veeola."

They deplaned and caught a cab into the city. The cab pulled up to a place with a sign of an eye ball.

"What are we doing here? Do you need to get your vision checked?" The salesman furrowed his eyebrows as he looked from the sign to the mentor.

"Just here to see an old friend. Come on!"

As they walked in, the salesman noticed the office was full of different types of people, and there was a line almost out the door. There were a couple of things that seemed strange to him. There were five men with some type of blindfold on walking around and bumping into things in the office. They were mumbling something, but it was hard to understand what they were saying. People acted like it was normal and paid them no attention. Everyone else in the office was upbeat and positive, but clearly the center of the attention was Veeola, the owner. She was a fairly tall woman with blonde hair, big personality, and a nice physique. As he walked around the room, he saw an emblem placed all around the office. He couldn't fully make it out until he walked up close to one on the wall. *Wait, is that a golden mailbox?* He was beginning to think she was the person with all the secrets. Maybe this was it. This was what he had been waiting for.

Veeola saw the mentor and was excited as they greeted one another with a hug like they were long lost sisters. "Who do we have here? Is this another salesman?" Veeola's voice commanded the room.

"Yes, it is! We are here to see you for the usual. Can you see us now?" The mentor winked at her friend.

"Absolutely! Anything for you. Come in my office and have a seat." Veeola locked arms with her friend as they walked into the office; the salesman followed behind.

Veeola inquired of her friend, "So, we have another salesman wanting success?"

The mentor nodded her head, and the salesman looked at both of them with a perplexed look on his face. Baffled by what he just witnessed in the lobby.

"Before you sit down young man, let me ask you a question. Do you even know what determines if you are successful or not? Have you thought about this?" Veeola questioned.

"Not really! I guess it's all about my numbers at the end of the month. If they look good then I'm good, and I won't stress out about not being able to pay my bills," he replied.

Veeola grabbed some tools from her desk and said, "Your numbers. Interesting! Okay, well let's do a few simple tests that should not take too long."

He sat in a big, comfortable, bright yellow chair. Veeola looked at him while holding some gadgets to test vision. She had him read off the letters from the chart.

The salesman, resuming his frustration, said, "I've got perfect vision. What are you doing? Just tell me about the emblem of the golden mailbox I saw out there on the bookshelf and on the walls."

Veeola and the mentor looked at one another and began speaking in Spanish. That was odd because Veeola didn't appear to be Hispanic. But, her accent and command of the

Spanish language were so unique. The room got quiet for about ten seconds, then the mentor spoke up.

"Veeola cannot tell you about that now. Remember you promised me you would take the four trips and then we would talk. Remember the four disciplines."

Veeola and the mentor walked out of the room. "I think you will need this." Veeola handed the mentor a bag of tea in a yellow homemade-looking pouch. The mentor took the tea and put it inside her purse.

The salesman, wanting to get the rest of the journey underway, raised his voice so they could hear him outside the room. "Okay, I'll stop asking questions. But you have to promise me you will tell me all your secrets and all this mailbox money stuff."

"You will know it all in due time. Please go along with the tests and do exactly as she asks of you." They walked back in the room and Veeola continued by showing him a chart with numbers on it. There was a group of nine numbers on the left, middle and right. Veeola asked him to repeat the numbers he had seen and try to group them as they were from his memory.

The salesman repeated some of the numbers but could not remember them all. He remembered a three and a five in the first group. Beyond that, he didn't remember much. She then showed him a different chart in which visual images replaced the numbers from the previous chart. For example, instead of the three, there was an owl. And, instead of the five, there was a lion. The salesman looked at the visuals and realized he could quickly understand and remember the images better than the numbers on the first chart. He remembered each image from the three groups which he couldn't do with the numbers. He asked questions about why the different groups had different images. The salesman could not help but to notice two of the images in the exercise were the golden mailbox and a regular mailbox. He was obviously much more engaged with the images than the numbers.

Veeola and the mentor looked at each other again as the salesman began to verbalize his understanding of the info back to them. Veeola went on to blurt out some interesting random statistics about visual images. She said, "The mind processes visual images sixty thousand times faster than they do text. High quality infographics are thirty times more likely to be read than plain text. People who follow instructions on video do three hundred and twenty-three percent better than those who follow text. The brain works with visual images, so this is what you have to do. You must play to the strength of how your brain functions," she tapped the side of her head.

The salesman sat up. "That makes sense. I can see how it helped me in this exercise, but what does this have to do with anything?"

Veeola stared him in the face to make her point. "Salesman, this has everything to do with it." Veeola grew more serious as they communicated more.

"Last exercise and the most important. Turn the lights down," Veeola said to the mentor as she lay him back in the chair, almost to a full lying down position. Veeola proceeded by putting something over the salesman's eyes to block his vision.

He looked at what she was about to put on his eyes and noticed it was the same thing over the eyes of the people in the lobby. Scared, he said, "I don't want that on my eyes. That's what those guys in the lobby had on their face. I don't want to turn into one of them."

The salesman was noticeably nervous so Veeola said, "I don't want you to be like them either, but you will not get to the golden mailbox without this last test. You must have some faith. Do you want it bad enough salesman?"

He nervously looked over at his mentor. She gave him an encouraging look and nodded her head. "Okay go ahead with it," he mumbled.

Veeola asked him to repeat the numbers from the first exercise. The salesman only repeated some of the information.

Then she asked him, "Repeat the images from the second exercise." He remembered mostly all of them. He clearly had better recollection of information from the second exercise. Veeola knew the salesman had been eating only fruits and nuts the past day and a half, so she said to him, "Clear your mind. I want you to imagine the perfect meal to eat. If it could be anything, what would it be? Take your time and think. I want details."

He fidgeted in the chair. He was a bit agitated. "I don't know what I want. It is hard for me to think about that lying here blindfolded. I am just wondering what this is all about. Why are we here? And, I don't want to turn into one of those people in the lobby. But if I have to pick something to eat I guess I would want the bag of potato chips I saw on the table earlier. It was one of my favorite flavors. Can I take off this mask now? Are we done?"

"A bag of chips? I know you haven't eaten, but you can't think of anything better that you desire? Think, please! Allow yourself to relax. You are so tense, and your feet have not stopped fidgeting since you laid down," Veeola replied.

The salesman calmed down a little and relaxed his legs and hands. His body became limber.

The salesman's stomach growled as he described his perfect meal. "The perfect meal. Okay! I want a steak medium-well with herb butter on the top, slightly pink inside. I want asparagus with the grill marks, and I want big steak fries cooked to perfection with the right crunch."

Veeola was excited that the salesman could see the meal so clearly. "Perfect! That is perfect. Tell me more."

The salesman's mouth salivated. "I am sitting next to the ocean and eating this meal as the waves are crashing in the background."

"Can you see it, salesman? Can you taste it?" Veeola clung to the salesman's vision like it was her own.

In a profound voice, the salesman shouts out, "I can taste it, and I want it."

Veeola walked in closer to him. "What type of plate is it on?"

"It's on a large, square white plate," the salesman drew a square with his index fingers.

Veeola clasped her hands together as she looked at the salesman. "Hold on to that vision, and when you go home find that restaurant and have that meal. You deserve it." She removed the mask from his eyes. "We are done here."

"That's it?" The salesman asked.

"It is time for us to go. We must leave before the weather turns." The mentor turned to hug Veeola, and the salesman followed suit. The mentor and Veeola spoke privately for a few minutes. Then she and the salesman jumped into a cab and headed back to the air strip where the plane was waiting.

CHAPTER 5

Peru Pakitza Region - Quiet Greatness

THE SALESMAN SAT ON the plane silently as they ascended and leveled off in the sky. "Where to now? I want this information so bad I can taste it. I'm getting impatient."

She said in due time they would be there.

"Be where?" He prodded.

"Peru in South America." There was a glint in her eye.

"Peru has to be it! The country has ruins and history, and I'm sure they have the golden mailbox or mailbox money somewhere. I just want to know what is in it." He was anxious. They then landed in another small, private airport close to the Manu National Park. They caught a ride from a local driver that the mentor knew, and the driver took them into the national park and dropped them off.

"Gracias señor," the mentor said to the driver as he pulled off.

There they were in the middle of this national park with

no one around. Curious, but still in amazement of being in Peru, the salesman queried, "Are we going to search for the golden mailbox now? Is it here?"

"I first want to show you something else."

As they walked around, the salesman noticed butterflies everywhere. "This place is amazing! I've never seen so many colorful butterflies in one place before. They are everywhere."

The mentor shared in his joy. "This place has more unique butterflies than anywhere else on Earth."

The salesman saw a caterpillar on the ground and lined up to stomp on it, but the mentor pushed him before he could.

"What are you doing? Did you see how big and ugly that bug was?" He asked her, astonished that she'd kept him from killing it.

"You have got to be kidding! That was a rare species that you almost killed," she shook her head at him.

"It's a nasty looking caterpillar. Look at it! It's disgusting!" Suddenly, the salesman pointed upward. "Look on the trees! Can you see that one?" He was amazed. "Wow, another! They are everywhere."

The mentor, seeing the amusement in the salesman's eyes, asked him, "Do you understand the full life cycle of the butterfly?"

"Not really. I remember something about it when I was in elementary school." He put his hand to his head in an attempt to think back.

"The stages of the butterfly are an absolute thing of

beauty, and you must know about this." The mentor grabbed the salesman's hands and looked into his eyes, "It is pretty simple. The egg is formed, the caterpillar comes next, then a cocoon, and lastly - the butterfly," she looked around at the butterflies flying overhead.

"Are you telling me that all these ugly caterpillars are going to go into a cocoon and fly away someday?"

"Yes, when their time is ready. If the process is disrupted, the full cycle does not happen." "The caterpillar is very small initially, then it begins to eat and eat, even eating the leaf that it was born on." The mentor shared the lesson with enthusiasm. "Caterpillars must shed their skin as they get bigger. The caterpillar sheds its skin three times or more while growing. The process is called molting."

"Did you say *molting*?"

"Yes! Molting is the name of this. It does not happen overnight. There are many stages that must happen. When this caterpillar is done growing, it creates what's called a Pupa. This is the stage of rest and transformation." Rest and transformation are critical at this stage, and if interrupted will stop the process of the caterpillar becoming a butterfly." The mentor was very knowledgeable about the stages of the butterfly.

"From this cocoon, as they call it, the butterfly comes out. And what you see here, all around us, are a result of this process. All the amazing colors, the beauty, these are the adult butterflies that will help to keep the process going," she explained.

"Can't believe I almost stepped on that caterpillar." The salesman was disappointed in himself.

The mentor smiled, patting him on the arm. "Give life. Do not take it. Respect the natural order and timing of things. Remember, trust the process!"

"Okay, I get it! Where to now? Let's keep moving." He was so anxious. He started to walk faster and looked around the forest to see if he saw anything that resembled ruins or a golden mailbox.

"Stop rushing for everything. You are constantly moving so fast and looking elsewhere that you are missing the beauty around you. The mailbox could be right here, and you would miss it. Relax, please! You are making me nervous," she frowned at him.

The salesman sat on a rock and gazed into the park's natural beauty. As he took it all in, the most colorful and rarest species of the butterfly landed on his leg. It was like a solid gold color with specks of red.

The mentor rushed over, telling him, "Don't move! That is a rare butterfly, and it is good luck. Make a wish."

The salesman closed his eyes and made his wish. When he opened them, he saw the butterfly peacefully fly away mixing in with the others. The mentor sat alongside him, and she could see that the trip was having a positive effect on him. He started the trip overly excited, and now she could see him beginning to relax.

"Would you mind telling me what you wished for?"

"I want to find the golden mailbox and mailbox money so bad. I just asked for clarity and hoped that you're not wasting my time." This time, there was no frustration in his voice. Just a sincere desire to find the golden mailbox.

"It will be clear, salesman. It will all be clear." She put her arm around him as they looked off into the distance.

Moments later they heard rustling in the woods. Out of nowhere, a large animal they had not seen before approached them. The salesman, startled, was about to run when the mentor grabbed his shoulder and put her finger over his mouth.

"Don't move!" Her voice was tense.

The salesman stood upright and held his breath. They both stood in front of the animal as it growled, saliva dripped from its mouth. The mentor stared right back, not giving up an inch.

"What do we do?" He whispered, scared for his life.

"Do you want the golden mailbox salesman?" She whispered back as she stared at the beast five yards from them.

"Golden mailbox? Are you serious? This animal is going to kill us!" He couldn't believe she would ask about the golden mailbox while they faced being ripped to shreds by this animal.

The mentor clapped her hands and yelled at the animal in Spanish. She yelled so fast that the salesman couldn't understand her. Suddenly, from the woods came a wild jaguar that chased the bear-like animal away. Both animals ran out of sight into the dense forest.

As the evening fast approached, they took a taxi back to the airport and prepared to leave Peru, and whatever they'd seen in the forest.

The salesman's nerves were still rattled. "What the heck was that? Why didn't you run? How did you know to do that? I was ready to run had you not grabbed me. Did you see the teeth on that animal?" He clung to his hands to keep them from shaking.

"Running would have gotten us in worse trouble. Sometimes standing firm is the best option. Did you think this journey to the golden mailbox would be easy? The closer we get to the golden mailbox, the more obstacles typically will appear," she said.

"Closer to the mailbox? I have not seen anything that even remotely looks like a mailbox since I've been with you. Where you have taken me, I've barely seen people. I just don't understand your logic." He shook his head.

"You will understand," she said in a hushed voice.

"You keep saying that, and nothing makes sense. Maybe I'm not meant to be here. Maybe this whole thing with mailbox money is fake."

The salesman slumped down in his seat as the taxi pulled up to the plane.

As they walked up to the plane, just like the last time, the pilot gave the salesman some nuts and snacks. The salesman took out the apple and ate the whole thing. He offered his remaining snacks to the mentor. The pilot gave a thumbs up to the mentor. She responded back to the pilot with a small smile and subtle thumbs up. Still, the mentor felt like she was losing the salesman's interest.

While on the plane, the salesman's anxiety returned. "Do you think the golden mailbox still exists? What if it's been moved and we cannot find it? Is that a possibility? Can you just tell me without us having to go to these different places?"

"Salesman, we made a deal about the four stops. Do you remember the four disciplines? We have one stop left. Just tell me do you want to continue or go home?"

He paused. There was silence on the plane. "Honestly, let's go home. This is a waste of time. There is no *golden mailbox*. I should get back to work." The salesman hung his head.

She lifted his chin. "Doing more of what you have done is going to get you more of what you have. You must change your way of thinking." The mentor told the pilot to take them home. The pilot looked back and gave the mentor a head nod acknowledging her request.

The plane ride home was quiet. The salesman looked out his window. The mentor wrote in her journal. When they arrived at their home airport, the mentor asked, "Can I offer you a ride? I have to pass your town first, and it will be an expensive cab fare."

"Sure! I'd appreciate saving the cab fare," he responded. "No hard feelings, ma'am. I still enjoyed the trip even though I didn't find what I thought I would. It was nice, and I'll be forever thankful for the experience."

They drove in her car, and as the mentor passed through the city she asked him, "Do you mind if I make a quick stop?"

"No! I don't mind since you're giving me a ride. I won't complain."

CHAPTER 6

La Tyme

THE MENTOR DROVE TO the local stadium for a fútbol (soccer) match. Driving through the crowd, she found a small parking spot on someone's property.

Puzzled, the salesman asked, "Why are we going to a fútbol game?"

"I love fútbol, and I follow the local team. This is a big game. Is that okay with you? I really don't want to miss it." She suspected he would be okay with it.

"I do like soccer, so I don't mind at all," he grinned at her.

They arrived at the game slightly after it had started, and they had amazing seats. Surprisingly, everyone around the area knew the mentor. She was greeted with hugs by many and even offered a complimentary pretzel - one of her favorite snacks. They watched the game as the home team, La Tyme, was ahead of its rival, Nona City Soccer Club. At the half, the score was 1-0.

"Salesman, do you know anything about La Tyme fútbol and their coach?" She asked.

"No, I do not follow the local teams. I watch the premier soccer league," he replied.

"This team we are watching, La Tyme, was one of the worst in the region for ten years. They made a head coaching change, and now the team is going for the championship against their rival, Nona City Soccer Club," said the mentor.

"Wow! What a turnaround! Just a head coaching change and they became that good?"

"The coaching change was just the start." She sat waiting for the teams to return to the field.

"Clearly there's more to their story. There is no way this team was one of the worst and with just a coaching change they are this good. They look amazing. Did you see how many times they passed to each other on that last score? Their vision and unselfishness are amazing."

"Yes! I saw it. This team started the year out average, and they seem to be winning at the right time. They've put themselves on the verge of winning a championship if they can beat Nona City. Good thing is they have won their last ten games, giving up no goals," she shared.

"La Tyme was coached for many years by the opposing coach of Nona City. He made a bold statement saying he knows everything about fútbol and these players from La Tyme were too dumb, and that this town was not ready to win." She scoffed.

At the half, both teams warmed up. Nona City was trying to impress the crowd by doing a series of complicated drills.

"Why does Nona City look like they are doing much more complicated drills than La Tyme? Nona City looks really good out there. La Tyme better be ready to play!" He huffed at the thought of La Tyme not practicing as strong as their opponent. "Look at our coach. He's out there with two cones having the team doing pretty basic offensive and defensive drills and strategy." He continued. "I will say, though, whatever he's saying to the team every player is paying close attention."

"Our players are focused." She chimed in before he could add anything else. "Yes, they are working on simple passing drills and basic concepts. Although it looks simple to you, the players have developed a great understanding of what they are doing." Her eyes never left the field as she watched La Tyme do their practice drills. "I've noticed how sometimes coaches overcomplicate things. They try to do more than they need to, literally coaching the team into defeat."

The La Tyme coach continued talking to his players on the sideline, his clipboard in his hands as he spoke to them. The salesman stared and noticed something on the coach's clipboard. "Is that a golden mailbox on the clipboard?" the salesman squinted and shook his head to ensure he was seeing correctly.

At the exact moment the salesman saw the golden mailbox on the clipboard, the coach looked up right to where they were sitting, pointed directly at the mentor and waived. She smiled and waved back at the coach.

"You know him, the coach from La Tyme?" The salesman was surprised. "He has a golden mailbox on his clipboard. Does he also know all the stuff?"

"Yes! He knows *the stuff*, as you call it. I have known the coach for a long time and actually met him and Veeola at the same time. Coach understands the four disciplines inside and out. I've learned lots from him. He is a wonderful person with a pure heart."

"It's like wherever we go this golden mailbox is following me. Even when I thought I had run from it; the mailbox shows up."

The La Tyme crowd was still energetic, chanting the coach's name as they prepared for kickoff. The salesman overheard the comments of some fans, "*The job Coach has done with these players is remarkable. He has taught them concepts, not just 'kick the ball and run.' I don't know how he did it but I'm happy,*" excitement was in their voices.

The game went back and forth with shots on goal from both teams, but the score was still 1-0 as the game wound down. With minutes left, Nona City Soccer Club took possession and set up an amazing series of passes, and they shot as the player beat the defender. The ball was in the air and the goalie dived and stretched to get his fingertips on the ball. It bounced off the cross bar and was kicked away by La Tyme as time ran out. The fans rushed the field and lifted up the coach carrying him off as La Tyme won the Championship. As they carried him off, fans began to chant, "*El Maestro, El Maestro.*"

"What are they saying? Who are they talking about?" Curiosity rang in the salesman's voice.

"They are calling the coach 'the teacher.' He brought a championship to our team and taught the players to win by coaching them the right way," she spoke while clapping for the team. Since the game ended, the mentor started walking out of the stadium and toward the car as they fought through the crowd of people.

"Tomorrow meet me at my office at seven thirty, and I will tell you my secret. Every question will be answered," she patted him on the back.

The salesman raised his eyebrows in response to what she'd just said. "Even though I left early after Peru you still want me to come?" He asked her, concerned she was playing a trick on him.

"Absolutely! I will see you tomorrow bright and early," said the mentor.

They drove and pulled up to a small apartment complex on the East side of town where the salesman lived. The mentor went in her purse and handed the salesman the pouch with the tea in it. "Salesman, it is important you drink this tea prior to our meeting. It will relax you from our trip and allow your body to rest. Drink it now, and I'll see you in the morning."

"I will! I need some tea. I'm exhausted," he yawned into

his sleeve. "I'll be there early. I have enough time to unpack and rest. I also wanted to say thanks although we didn't, you know, find the golden mailbox, it was still pretty cool. At least I've been on a private plane now," said the salesman. The mentor hugged him, walked back to the driver's side door, got in and closed the door.

She opened the passenger window, "One thing before I go. Some things may not make sense to you later. I'm sure you will have questions. When we meet tomorrow, I promise I will explain everything."

"What do you mean 'not make sense'?" He looked at her with raised eyebrow. "Like I said, I am going to drink this tea and go to bed. I will see you tomorrow," he walked toward his door.

As he put his key in his door, she yelled, "Salesman, do not forget what I said. I will explain in the morning." He waved her off and smiled as he walked inside.

CHAPTER 7

The Dream

THE SALESMAN SETTLED INTO being home. He unpacked his suit-case and made some food to go along with his tea. He was tired from all the travel, and it caught up to him. After eating and drinking the tea, he took a seat in his favorite chair. Before he knew it, he was in a deep sleep. This sleep was like none other, and he would not be the same after.

In this dream the salesman was in his dream house. The house had all the things he wanted - wood floors, crown molding, several bedrooms and bathrooms, and a huge kitchen. He decided to go outside to see if it was as perfect as the inside. It was noticeably peaceful with big trees and nice landscaping. He saw something glowing amidst the trees. Drawing closer to it, he realized it was a golden mailbox.

"It is here!" He shouted in the air. "It is real!" He was overcome with happiness. He looked at himself through the shiny reflection in the mailbox. Suddenly, he looked up and realized he wasn't alone. Not only was he not alone, there was a long line of people at the mailbox – *his* mailbox. The salesman said to someone in the line, "I'm sorry! I've been looking for this mailbox, and I've found it. It's mine!"

He stared through squinted eyes and realized he recognized the first person standing in line. "Erin is that you?" He stared in disbelief.

She looked at him and responded, "Good morning! Thanks again for all your help." Erin approached the mailbox, put money inside and walked off.

The salesman then noticed Trisha Jones and Keith Jackson. They approached him, also thanking him, and put money inside the mailbox. Random amounts of money were being put inside the mailbox. Some people put in fifty cents, and others put in hundreds of dollars. Mrs. Steele, another of his clients, put in multiple amounts of money when it was her turn to go to the mailbox. At one point, the salesman had to fix the mailbox because there was so much money inside. When he went to fold the money, he was overjoyed because he hadn't felt that much money in a long time.

"*Mailbox Money!* This is it!" He mumbled to himself and stared at the wad of money in his hands.

The line stretched all the way around the corner, and one by one, for the next three hours the line moved, and everyone put money inside the mailbox. David McMillan said, "I'll see you again next month. Have a good day!" The salesman thought to himself, "*Next month? Is this going to happen again?"*

The line finally died down, and the salesman saw that trash and weeds began accumulating by the mailbox. He immediately bent down and picked up the trash and pulled the weeds out. The salesman took off his shirt and wiped all the fingerprints and smudges from the mailbox. The mailbox was sparkling again, just as it was when he had seen it in the morning. He cleaned the entire area and made it better than before.

He heard a voice from the mailbox say, "Thank you, salesman!"

Startled, he jumped back and looked around. "Hello? Who's there?" He asked and looked toward the mailbox.

"It is me, salesman! Thank you so much!" came the voice from the mailbox.

"Can you really talk?" The salesman was baffled.

The voice spoke again, "Of course salesman! You just have to listen to me. Thank you for cleaning me and picking up those weeds in the grass."

"My pleasure! I mean, this is crazy! I knew all those people in the line. They were all my clients, and now you are talking to me. I don't know what to make of all this," he rubbed his hand across his forehead.

"Respect me, care for me, and I will definitely care for you back," the golden mailbox spoke.

"I will do more than care for you. I will praise you, golden mailbox."

"*Praise me*? Be careful salesman. I have a master much more important than I. I am just your golden mailbox. Always give thanks in all things, but don't praise the material in which it shows up."

The salesman, in shock, stepped back from the mailbox and immediately dropped to his knees. As he did this, the wind began to blow, and the trees swayed in the breeze. The insects began to make an unusual noise. Then he saw it. The golden butterfly from Peru landed right in front of him on the mailbox. After ten seconds, the butterfly peacefully flew away. It was as if all the positive energy of the world was with him in this moment. The sky became crystal clear, the sun shone brightly, and the most refreshing rain began to fall.

The salesman, wet from the rain, cried out, "I'm thankful! I'm grateful! I thank you so much for all things. I am blessed!" As he stood, the rain immediately stopped. "Golden Mailbox, can you hear me?" He spoke to the mailbox.

The voice that had come from the mailbox was gone. In its place was a deafening silence.

"Mailbox, are you there? I just heard you," the salesman shouted. He went to open the mailbox, and it was sealed shut. He pulled on it with all his might, and just then, the salesman jumped up from his sleep. When he realized he had been asleep, he immediately looked to check the time, but the clock was flickering.

"My goodness! The power went out. What time is it?" He jumped from under the covers and ran to grab his phone to check the time. "Wow! It's only five thirty in the morning," he said to himself. Confused from the dream, all the salesman could think of was what was in that tea he drank, and the meeting he was supposed to have that morning with his mentor. She had to be able to explain to him what was going on in the dream. It was so real, it was like he was there. Never had the salesman dreamed like that with such a sense of truth and reality.

. . . .

CHAPTER 8

The Meeting

AT SEVEN FIFTEEN, THE salesman arrived at the mentor's office. She looked pleasantly surprised to see the salesman fifteen minutes early. She asked him, "How did you rest?"

The salesman looked at her with a surprised look on his face. "Why did you ask that? Do you know about the dream I had?" His eyes were wide as he looked to her for answers.

"I have a dream like that almost daily, young salesman," she gave him a soothing smile.

"What does it mean? I have so many questions," he took a seat.

"I am here for you salesman. I promised you I would tell you my secret," she crossed her hands in front of her on the desk.

The salesman sat up, and you could see his nervous energy bubbling up. "Okay, my first question - was the golden mailbox real? I saw it. I touched it. There was rain in the dream, and I could feel it. It was all so real," he touched his face to be sure he wasn't still in the dream.

"The golden mailbox is real. The mailbox money being put in was real. The line outside was real. Salesman, do you realize when you get paid monthly many people make up the check you get?" She asked him.

"I haven't thought of it like that," he sat back in the chair.

"When you saw that mailbox and the people lined up, you became overjoyed when you saw the money going in, didn't you?"

"Yes! I saw it, touched it. I definitely was overjoyed," he put his elbows on the desk again.

"When you thought about the line outside, did it make you want more people in the line?"

"Absolutely! Of course; I wanted more people in the line when I realized they were putting money in the mailbox. I wanted to make sure the mailbox was clean and organized. I even pulled weeds," he told her.

The mentor laughed out loud. Once she calmed down, she got up from her chair and stood next to the salesman. "Envision your clients as if they were standing outside your house one by one putting money into your mailbox month after month. This actually happens, but we do not physically see it. When you saw this in the dream, you became changed. You must see every person that pays you lined up outside. By seeing that visual it will allow your golden mailbox to come to life and get filled with mailbox money," she waved her hands like an orchestra conductor.

"So, you're telling me your secret is thinking about your clients outside your mailbox, and that is how you've become successful?"

"Yes! That is exactly what I'm telling you. One person will lead to two, and then two to four, and so on. Keeping this vision is going to allow you to cater to your clients and build better relationships in a way you have never done before." She sat down and continued. "You are probably forgetting about people in your business that could help take you to the next level. You want to make sure people continuingly come to your mailbox and put in as much money as they can month after month. You will want them to bring friends to your mailbox as well."

"Bring friends to put money in my mailbox? That would be nice," his eyes grew wide.

"It will happen if you think of it. But the number one thing you need to focus on is how many of those already coming to your golden mailbox are making one deposit or only have one product with you," she said.

"Well, I typically sell the one thing my clients ask for, and that's it. After they buy it then I'm done. I don't want to bombard them with other products," he confessed. "Well, if they really needed anything else, then they would contact me."

"You're thinking is all wrong. You are in the business of helping people, not pushing products. Everything you offer can help people. Some people may have multiple problems but because of your fear, you are only helping them with one. They don't even know you have the ability to help them with more. They leave your mailbox and go across the street to someone else's mailbox to put money in to fulfill their other needs." The mentor was dumbfounded the salesman hadn't thought of this. "Your clients want *you*. They just don't know what you can and cannot do for them. So, when you ask, try to be helpful and not scared. You will find that many of these people coming to your mailbox need more help from you. This will lead to people making multiple deposits into your golden mailbox.

....

CHAPTER 9

Multiple Ways

"ON MY JOURNEY TO my mailbox money, I was taught that you should have seven different ways people can put money into your mailbox. It can all be in the same profession, or different revenue streams. By having various ways money can go into your mailbox, you protect yourself in the event one revenue stream dries up. I have seen far too many people have one stream of mailbox money and something happens to that stream that causes the mailbox money to be reduced. Major corporations own different companies that you may not know about. They are protecting themselves from the danger of one source of revenue. You should do the same. Go from one stream to two, not one to seven. Start by better servicing your clients in the portfolio you are most comfortable with. Then you can think of other businesses or ways to get mailbox money," she made him think.

"The truth is, I've been scared of asking people more

JOE FERRER

questions. I settle with what they want once they agree to do business with me," he laid his hands in his lap.

"Have you heard the saying 'ABC?'" She questioned.

"Always be closing?" He countered back.

"No! It stands for Always Be Creating. Never hesitate to think of new ideas and strategies to be successful in your business. Never stop creating and thinking of alternative business ideas that may be good to invest in or create for yourself." The mentor got excited. "With the help of the disciplines, this creativity will potentially allow you to create completely different mailboxes within their own lines and further your grasp of the mailbox money concept."

She continued, "Not sure if I told you this, but I own properties and another business as well. I wouldn't have done this if I hadn't gained the knowledge of mailbox money and the power of creating a line that will grow exponentially, of people, at my mailbox. In my other business, I don't even have to physically be there, and my line gets longer each month." She encouraged him. "Please hear me clearly. I'm not saying for you to go out and create a million ideas. Find success in yourself, in who you are. Then, be open to creating. The fear of asking people for more than one thing when they need it, and the fear of not wanting to create anything will stunt the growth of your mailbox money."

She paused and looked up. "You will be free of that fear now that you know the disciplines and the concept of mailbox money. These disciplines will combat your fear and prepare you for greatness, young salesman," she smiled anticipating what the salesman would say next.

"I don't know all the disciplines. Are you sure I'm ready?" He stood and paced the floor.

"I will continue to explain to you everything, but the disciplines are in you. You have gained great wisdom."

"Sounds odd because I can't tell you one of the disciplines, and you are telling me I know all four?" He stood still to look his mentor in the eyes. The salesman put his finger on his head as if trying to remember something.

"Did you have a question that you cannot remember?"

He paused for a minute, then finally remembered. "Oh yea! Why did the mailbox talk to me? Does your mailbox talk to you?"

"Our business is always talking to us. You must be willing to listen when it does. An example could be as simple as you arriving at seven thirty in the morning for our meetings when you didn't want to meet earlier than eight thirty. Something inside you told you it was important. Don't neglect this voice. Your business will guide you if you focus on the mailbox money vision."

"I sure *did not* think I could get up that early. I haven't been at meetings that early since fútbol practice in college," said the salesman.

"When you made the decision to follow me on the journey to the golden mailbox and learn about mailbox money, what happened is the power of the golden mailbox began to open doors and opportunities for you. Your mailbox wants you, but before it wants you, you must first want it. Remember you came to my office and asked how you could be successful and what my secret was? That was the true first step toward your journey. That is when your golden mailbox began to call on you," she helped him begin to understand.

"*Call me?* Wow! This is deep. I feel important. I've never felt like this before," he shrugged and shook his head.

"This is extremely deep, and the more you understand, the deeper it gets. Everything that happened on the trip was your personal journey to your golden mailbox. Each person can learn the disciplines, but how it comes about may be different."

"Seems like this golden mailbox is powerful," he rubbed his chin as he thought about it.

"Yes, it is! The greatest people in business understand that mailbox money is the reason for success at small and large companies. The four disciplines are amazing and can be applied in all aspects of business, sports, and life," she encouraged him.

The salesman put his finger on the side of his head again, trying to recall something. "Another question - why did my mailbox tell me that he had a master? That was confusing."

"I'll explain briefly. There is a higher force that people pray to. This force is the creator of the whole world and is ultimately in control of your golden mailbox," the mentor appeared tranquil as she shared her knowledge.

"So, is that the *master* that the golden mailbox was referring to in my dream?"

"Yes! You got it. Also, you cannot have a true golden mailbox and mailbox money if you treat others poorly and are not kind and forgiving. If you lack these things, your mailbox will eventually crumble," said the mentor.

"Would you believe, for the first time in my life, I just volunteered at my church for the whole summer? I helped teach and tutor kids from poor neighborhoods. This summer my focus was on trying to be a better person. It was on my way home from tutoring, after I spent many hours with the kids, that I thought about how I would be able to give more than just my time. I want to know more about *how* to give. Am I going about it the right way? I want to give more financially, so I need to make more money first. To do that, I thought about you as the most successful person I know," he smiled at her.

The mentor paused and sat. By the pensive look on her face, she looked like she was going through a mental timeline in her head. She finally spoke. "Everything makes perfect sense now. The morning you came in to see me, I was scheduled to go to a meeting out of town, and that meeting was rescheduled at the last minute." She smiled. They both sat quietly for a brief moment as they realized that their meeting was not coincidental.

THE DISCIPLINES

....

STAY CLOSE TO THE PROCESS

"OKAY, ALL THIS IS making much more sense," the salesman was connecting the dots. "But, I still have lots of questions. What exactly are the four disciplines you said I learned, and what was the purpose of our trip? I still don't remember you going over them with me."

"All the disciplines were taught, and you learned them on our trip. These disciplines allow you to understand your golden mailbox and make mailbox money," the mentor tried jogging the salesman's memory. "You would not have had the dream had you not learned the disciplines."

"What did I gain on our first stop? All I remember was the mountain and sleeping in the woods. What did I gain from that? Did you want me to learn how to sleep in the woods?" He laughed.

The mentor laughed with him, then got to the point. "What you gained was the first discipline, discipline numero uno, of learning about being too far removed from the process and learning to connect." She leaned in. "Pay close attention. Do you remember how far you walked for that water? Do you remember how you appreciated it afterward?"

"That *was* the best water I ever had," the salesman chuckled. "Remember that apple was so hard for me to get to in the tree? I sure did appreciate that as well, more than the first apple I barely ate before throwing it over the mountainside."

"Good, salesman, you are getting it. When people hunted for food hundreds of years ago, they utilized every part of the animal, barely any waste. Animals were used for their skins, meat and much more. This was because people worked hard for the food, and food was not in abundance or as easy to get as it is now," she made the picture clearer for the salesman. "Today, if we order food and don't like it, we can throw it away because it is fairly easy to get more food from the many restaurants that are available. We are no longer connected, so it's easy to throw things away without thinking about it. Translate this to your money. Think about what happens when you get paid. Your money goes directly to your bank, and you have money in your bank account waiting. You did not have to go to the bank, stand in line and sign the check to make the deposit," she clarified. "You are not connected to the process of how your money got there. Understanding how your money got there is a crucial part of the process. Am I making sense? Do you understand me, salesman?" She asked.

"You are making sense. This is something I never thought about. I *am* far removed in my business. I am so caught up trying to gain new clients that I've forgotten all the steps that need to take place before money even hits my account." His face grew sad. "I have forgotten those that pay me regularly, that allow me to run a practice."

The mentor chimed in. "Imagine people hunting for food and they kill an animal to only use one part of the animal and leave the rest to rot. When you're close to the process and you get a client, you get to know all the things that they need help with, and that you could do much more for them. By staying close to the process with your clients, you can embrace the deposits in your mailbox."

She added, "Remember when you had to work to get the apples in the tree and the water in your thermos? It forced you to appreciate normally simple things at a different level. When you slept outside it made you appreciate the beauty of safety and protection. Take nothing for granted, salesman." She added, "On pay day, make sure you are aware of the clients that make up the dollar amount you get. This is how you stay close to the process. Being aware of each person will help you to remain thankful. This newfound wisdom will help you to reconnect with your clients and service them better. By keeping close to the process and staying engaged, you will remember those in your business who are important and those who were difficult to acquire. You now will fight to keep each one because you understand and appreciate them, and it is easier to keep these clients than to get new ones," she reminded him.

"I now understand I need to stay close to my process. I truly have lost track of this with my clients and my support staff and even the process of how I get paid," he grappled with the reality of his words.

"Your clients are like water. You need them to live, and they must be treated as such. Bend over backwards for them and make sure you understand every process from top to bottom that has to deal with your clients. Since I found my golden mailbox I reach out to my clients one way or another twelve times a year. Sometimes a call, and sometimes a simple note. These interactions allow my clients to understand that they truly matter to me. When they know they matter to me, they happily come to my mailbox. What you want are happy people at your mailbox. The best companies have mastered the art of customer service and even if their price is higher, the service they provide will have you happily put money in that business' mailbox," she explained.

"To be honest, I have also lost being close to the process with my own family and those who have done so much for me. This vision of my golden mailbox will not only change my business forever, but my entire life and how I look at things." He took a deep breath. "Now that I think through it, you did teach me the first discipline," he smiled at his mentor.

"I had done the same thing with my family many years ago. My son, at one point, was struggling in school. I told him to do his work every day as I did my work. We fought and fought about his work daily. At that time, I was busy struggling in this career trying to be successful. I wondered why he was not succeeding when I would try my best to be on top of him. I thought about the first discipline, and rather than telling him to do school work, I actually put my work down and did his homework with him. I needed to be involved and close to the process, and that involvement is what changed my life and his. He told me later that the most fun he had was studying with me. I then learned I needed to spend more time with him studying not just telling him what to do. Now he is a scholar, and I'm proud of him," she grinned from ear to ear.

Continuing after reflecting, she advised, "Don't forget about how you get paid. You must understand how the mailbox money comes. When you understand that, you will figure out ways to maximize your mailbox money. Remember what I said about the vision. You must really see the people in your line in front of the mailbox and understand who pays you and how often you get paid. Failure to know how much you are paid through all your streams could lead you down the wrong path. Maybe what you're offering is not profitable? Maybe some of it is a waste of time? Evaluate your offerings regularly so you will know. Also stay close to the process and understand your contracts, so when a company offers you something like switching to a new compensation plan you can make a wiser choice, and not just go with what others are pushing. You will know more and make the right decision."

The salesman looked intently as the mentor continued.

"Another very important thing for you to know is once you make the right choices and get to the point of being successful, you must recognize that is only half the battle. The other half is to stay successful," she pointed her finger into her desk to emphasize her point. "Remember the tree, Mama Earth, we visited when we were on the mountain? Think of that tree as your business. It could grow to be huge and have tremendous success. Failing to pay attention and staying close to the process could result in your business crashing quickly one day, just like Mama Earth did. Many things could cause this to happen. The point is, just because it took long to build and grow, doesn't mean it can't come down in seconds without warning.

"Now I understand that these disciplines are not just about business, they are about life," he said.

"No, you learned it. Not everyone that goes through these experiences understands it the way you did. Give yourself some credit," she patted his hand.

"Okay! I got it! Discipline number one - stay close to the process, especially with your clients and understanding your mailbox money. Will you now tell me about the second discipline?" He was taking it all in.

....

THE POWER OF VISUALIZATION

"DO YOU REMEMBER VEEOLA?" His mentor asked.

"Of course, I remember her and the eye test. What does she have to do with the mailbox money?" He was confounded again.

"What do you remember most about that meeting in her office?"

"Honestly, those weird people in the lobby. They scared me."

"Oh! Yes, the visionless people with no vision of their future," she remembered.

"Can they actually see?" He recalled how odd they seemed.

"They probably can see better than both of us but have no true vision of their future. There are a bunch of people walking around this office right now like that - without that mask on. You were more like those people than you thought you were. The visionless go to Veeola to learn her secrets so they can be successful. But other than, as you call it, the 'weird people' what else stood out for you?"

"I remember that perfectly cooked steak that she had me think about. I have reservations to a restaurant tonight that supposedly has the best steak in town. The taste is still in my mouth since the trip. You should join me."

"Not tonight, salesman. This meal you should have alone. It is your vision, and by being alone you will truly connect with your mailbox money vision." She wanted him to know that sometimes you have to carry out your vision on your own.

The salesman rubbed his stomach. "Okay, but it's going to be good."

The mentor shifted his mind from the steak. "Back to Veeola. Remember all the images she showed you, all the numbers and animals on the chart? But what you remember most vividly was the mental image that you created of the food. The second discipline you learned was creating the vision in your head and seeing it as yours. This power of the visualization discipline is very important with mailbox money as you must create visuals only you can see. Prior to ever realizing the success you want to have, visualization is the first step. I want you to see yourself more successful than I am, and I want you to believe it can happen."

"*Better than you*? Are you serious?" The salesman couldn't believe he could be better than his mentor.

"Stop that now!" Her cheeks got red. "I was once like you.

Far from the one who is standing before you today. I was taught the same principles of mailbox money from a wise teacher, and since then, my line of clients at my mailbox has never been the same. That is why the mental visual of your mailbox is key. You must be able to see your line. Only you will know what it looks like and how fast it will grow. She closed her eyes as she continued. "You must visualize that line as small, then see the line grow larger and larger until you will need multiple mailboxes to satisfy the demand."

She opened her eyes to find that the salesman had closed his. "Visualization will give you hope through the rough times. This is a discipline that must be mastered as it will be utilized often. Your constant visions of people at your mailbox will keep you motivated when other circumstances tell you otherwise. Envision all the details of your mailbox money and golden mailbox, the size of your mailbox, the types of people in your line. Think about the different reasons they will be putting money inside. Also, think of the reasons people are not in your line now, and how you can change that. Think of your mailbox in different time frames. How does the line look one year from now? How does it look five years from now? Looking at your mailbox money in different timeframes is a healthy exercise that you must do at least twice monthly, if not more," she said.

"Salesman," she continued. "When it comes to visualization, think of what it felt like on the mountain where everything at the bottom of the mountain appeared to be so tiny. If you had binoculars, you would have been able to see everything clearly. The binoculars would have given you a different vantage point. Some people only see what's right in front of them; they are not future-focused. Even when your vision doesn't seem clear, imagine having on permanent binoculars that allow you to see your vision a year from now...five years from now... and as far into the future as you want. That is what the power of visualization allows you to do."

"That's a good way to think of it! So, what was the point of the numbers and trying to make me remember them? What was that about," asked the salesman. "Tell me more about why Veeola asked me to remember the pictures of animals and images. That was kind of weird. What does that have to do with mailbox money?"

"Veeola was teaching you another powerful element of this second discipline. What she taught you was the power of images in comparison to numbers. People think numbers are everything, and although they are important, visual imagery can be just as powerful, if not more powerful. That is why your mailbox that you envision is golden. The powerful image is what mailbox money is all about." The mentor could see the salesman was listening intently. "If you focus on the visual image of yourself being successful, the numbers will take care of themselves. You must act as if you have already achieved it and it will happen. Create the habits of what your better life looks like. Think of your business goals and apply images to them to make them real. This was taught to me, and I use it all the time. I can grasp images better because I understand that is how my brain works. When I have a goal to travel somewhere, I put up a picture of that place where I can see it daily. That image reminds me of where I want to go. I see myself in the picture as if I am there now. This vision motivates me to make it a reality," she shared to help inspire him.

"My head is going to explode with this new information. This is life changing. Why didn't I know this before? Everyone needs to know this. We must tell everyone about this," he sat at the edge of his seat.

"Easy! Slow down, young salesman. You are forgetting what I just told you earlier," she wagged her finger. "This is something you must be ready to receive, and when the time is right for someone, the teacher will appear. If I would have told you this two years ago you would have brushed me off and thought I was talking foolishness. Focus on yourself and stay true to your vision for now. Once you have mastered mailbox money, you will know when the time is right to share it with someone else."

"For now, think back to the steak. Remember how you were salivating over it. You could almost taste it. Now you have the ability to visualize and see yourself as that perfect steak cooked to perfection. Create the mental image of you being successful with the best qualities that you would ever want. The steak is you, salesman. How you visualized that meal, make your vision of success more real than that. What has stopped you is your continued focus on what is right in front of you and you have been comparing yourself to others. This has stopped you from truly being able to visualize your future. Your vision is for you and only you. Don't compare someone's success with yours. This will only frustrate you and limit you from your future. Today, someone can be ahead of you, but tomorrow can be your day."

"Coach, from La Tyme, spent a lot of time with his players before games and all they did was focus on the second discipline of visualization. They imagined every goal, every pass; the players saw themselves playing the game at a higher level. What ended up happening was the players actually got close to or exceeded what they had seen many times in their visions. Coach told me that before the season began, they spent an hour just focusing on what it would feel like thirty seconds after winning the league championship. That is why all the players were so emotional after the game. They were experiencing the powerful manifestation of the discipline of visualization." Her eyes glimmered as she shared the story.

"Mentor, for the first time in a long time I feel really good. I can see myself successful in the future. I know it will happen," he, too, had a glimmer in his eye as he thought about manifesting his vision.

....

TRANSFORMATION

"BEFORE I GO ANY further, I want to apologize for some of my actions and attitude about this trip. I know I have not been easy to deal with, and before we continue on, I want to say thank you for being patient with me. I apologize for everything," the salesman looked to the mentor for assurance that she would accept his apology.

She shook her head in agreement. "I must agree. You have not been the easiest to take on this journey, and I do accept your apology. Owning and acknowledging your mistakes is a big deal. I knew I liked you for a reason, young salesman.

The salesman felt better. He stood as he talked to the Mentor. His voice was louder and more confident as they spoke. "My favorite trip was probably when we saw the butterflies in Peru. Tell me about that. It obviously was one of the four disciplines, right?"

"How soon do you want success, salesman?" his mentor asked.

"I want it now! This job is taking way too long for me to make the money other people make. I have a good friend that's making much more money than me on his job, and a week ago I thought about leaving this job and going to where he works," he spoke hastily.

"You have only been working here for two years. The work that we do is not a get-rich-quick scheme. It takes time! It takes patience to build relationships with clients that will bring you the success you desire. When I first started in this business, I wanted quick money, too. I had little mouths to feed, and I wanted fast money to support my family. My husband's job wasn't paying much at the time, so I had to work to help us stay afloat." She shared intimate details with him about her family to help him understand why she wanted quick money. "But I learned in sales, it's all about the process. Knowing the process of getting and keeping clients and helping them understand what they need and how you can support them in obtaining that. If I could learn and apply that, then you can, too! So, why would you leave knowing this?

"He said I could make more money with him, and I want more," he told her the truth.

"Money is only part of the equation. Your life is your own, salesman. Don't let someone else take you away from your mailbox. Nor should you purposely take someone from theirs.

Do you remember in Peru when we saw the eggs that turned into the caterpillars? We saw these caterpillars walking and eating leaves, and you almost stepped on one because you said it looked pretty nasty," she reminded him.

"Yes, I do! I remember you pushed me out of the way then told me about their lifecycle," he remembered vividly.

"Salesman, that lifecycle is called *transformation* or *metamorphosis* as it relates to the caterpillar. We start out as eggs and then we become caterpillars." Her words provided visualization. What do caterpillars do all the time? Do you remember what I told you?"

"You told me that in the first part of their transformation, all they do is eat and eat, get bigger and shed their skin two to three times."

"Exactly! You need to eat and acquire knowledge, learn what you can from the experts. Continuing to feed your brain will cause you to expand and shed your own skin as you grow. Become an expert at what you do. Surround yourself with others that strive for what you want. The quality of people in your line will be linked to your level of expertise. The transformation to becoming an expert is what makes you referable, which increases the amount of people that desire to be in your line. This increased knowledge will help you to get ready for the stages of transformation," said the mentor.

The salesman's excitement grew. "I remember seeing the butterflies and being amazed at their beauty, but what you are saying is being a butterfly is the last step of transformation. It takes a process to get there, and it does not happen overnight."

"I took you to Peru because you had to realize that the process in business is not always going to be pretty in the beginning. Remember when you thought the caterpillar was ugly?" She asked, not giving him a chance to respond. "Maybe it was, but it had to go through the transformation like your business will. There will be many sleepless nights, as you may already know. Trust me, it gets better with focus and dedication. Unlike you, when I saw that caterpillar I knew that it would become a beautiful butterfly. So, when others look at you they may see a struggling salesman. I, on the other hand, see a young man destined for greatness. You will fly, and when you do, I'll be there to see you soar." Tears formed in the corners of her eyes.

"This is really starting to sink in. Mailbox money is a mentality. It is a way of life." He finally was convinced.

The mentor stood to her feet and gave the young salesman a high five. She became noticeably emotional as a tear ran down her face. "People want to be butterflies, salesman. But they don't have the patience and understanding to know they must be transformed first. This transformation takes different amounts of time for different people. Mine and yours is different, and that is why no two butterflies are exactly the same. If any part of this transformation is rushed, the butterfly may never fly. I want you to fly like a butterfly. Be happy where you are in your process and understand your time to fly will come." She took a breath. "Mailbox money takes time and, like I said, it is not a get-rich-quick mentality. You are building your mailbox one deposit at a time - brick by brick," she inspired him.

"It won't be perfect," she said. There will be mistakes that you will make. There will be times you feel like you've failed, but these things are part of your journey toward your golden mailbox. What you will realize in the future is that each of those mistakes were necessary. Find the lesson in everything you do and write down your mistakes so you don't make them again. Remember to write down your solutions, too, so you can reference them later. The small mistakes you make now will save you much more in the future if you learn the lesson. Learning these lessons will get you closer to the ultimate success you want."

"I know it is hard to imagine this type of success when you look at where you are and do not think that it is attainable. Just think, salesman, the office building we are in is thirty-four stories high and magnificent. This building is the premier building in our city. I remember when it was being built and there was just dirt on the ground. Slowly I began to see the transformation of the building that we see today. Think of your business the same way and build it brick by brick, and one day you will have all the clients you can handle. Embrace transformation; don't focus on your current status.

The salesman was focused on the mentor, holding onto her every word. He barely blinked as he listened. "I better call my friend about that job offer. There is no way I am going to leave now." He felt exhilarated. "I realize I am growing my business, and to quit now would not be smart. I could become a caterpillar that never got to fly." His revelation jolted him. "With this third discipline I understand true success is a process and takes time. I know there are stages, and I must go through each of them to be transformed and better in what I do," he said.

"I don't know your future for certain, but I know this understanding of mailbox money will change you and guide you in life and business," she smiled at him the way a loving mother would.

....

THE POWER OF APPLIED INFORMATION

AS THEY CONTINUED TO talk and reflect, the mentor dabbed her eyes with tissue as they both stood in the office.

The salesman continued to reflect as he prepared for the final discipline. "The only other thing I remember was the fútbol match. That could not have been one of the four disciplines because we were on our way home after I stopped the trip early," he thought aloud.

She chuckled under her breath. "You did not stop the trip early. I knew you were going to want to go home at that exact time. It was destined to happen that way. Many people stop chasing a dream right before they get all the answers and rewards," she stepped in closer to him. "Unfortunately, many of the other salesmen, like you, who have come to me for mentorship didn't make it as far as you did. Imagine if you would have wanted to go home after our first trip to the mountain. You would have missed all this information about mailbox money and the golden mailbox, and you would have had to take the long way to success."

"So that is what you meant by taking the long way? You meant me trying to figure it out on my own without this mailbox money knowledge?" The salesman got it. "Wow! I almost quit, and I would have probably had the same issues at the next company."

"Trying to go it alone is a rough path and could lead you somewhere you do not want to be. Seek wise council and listen when someone speaks knowledge to you," she shared.

"I'm so grateful you taught me this. I can see how people try to do things on their own and continue to repeat failures," the salesman said.

"It happens all the time. You are not the only one that I have taken on the journey," the mentor shared. "But, you are one of the few that now understands mailbox money and have seen the golden mailbox," she told him.

The salesman perked up, remembering something. "But what about the fútbol match? What was the reason for that?"

"What a game! What you saw was a team that was the worst for many years, and a coach came along, took the same players and brought them to win a championship," the mentor spoke with admiration for the coach. "What he was able to do was provide them with the same information they had heard so many times before but in a manner that made sense to them. He is well known for using stories to help him get his message across when coaching. Another thing that I know you picked up on is that rather than work on many formations, he has the team focus on one offensive and one defensive drill. He felt that by mastering the simpler formations, the team would be better. And, they were."

"My mentor was the same way," the mentor continued. "When I wanted to learn many different things, he constantly reminded me to get really good in one area before jumping to the next. Naturally, we want to learn and do so much, but simplicity wins. This one idea helped jump start my mailbox money and keep it flowing."

The salesman sat down, quietly paying attention as she spoke. "You see, information is out there, but what makes this coach great is he gets the players to understand the information and apply it in the match. Without proper application, it doesn't matter what you think you know. Every coach in fútbol can do the same drills or run the 4-4-2 or 3-3-4 formation," she said. "The point is, these formations mean nothing if the players do not know each other's responsibility as it relates to the formation. So, find a way to take the information you learn in business and deliver it in a way that gets your clients to take action. When clients take action, your mailbox money grows," she enlightened him.

"I don't understand. La Tyme looked really good. Did they have bad coaches in the past?" He was curious.

"Quite the opposite. They had one of the best and highest paid coaches in league history. But, not one coach before this new one had success here," said the mentor.

"Why? If they were the best coaches, why couldn't they win here, but this new coach did?" asked the salesman.

"These players are from the worst area of town, and this coach understands how to take his information and teach them in a way that they understand. No other coach tried to understand the players. All they did was shove information or drills down the players' throats. The players may be good, but if they don't understand why they are doing something, they probably won't have success." She continued to school the salesman. "The team is good now because they understand what Coach wants and expects from them. His stories resonated with them. The players always acknowledge that El Maestro is a great communicator. The players finally understand the way fútbol should be played," said the mentor.

"So, you are telling me just because I study the work material and know my products inside and out, I am not guaranteed success?" He looked at her like she was speaking another language.

"That is exactly what I am saying. Most people have access to the same information. It is about those that take that information and use it correctly. The coach from Nona City could have tried to do the same offense as La Tyme did. It would not guarantee his success. Think about you and I as salespeople in the office. We went through the exact same training program. I have just utilized the information differently than you. You must know who you are talking to and take your information and form it in a way your clients will understand. The information means nothing if you cannot move clients to action," she told him.

"Why did he have the golden mailbox on his clipboard if he is not a business man?" The naïve salesman pondered.

"Remember, mailbox money is not just about business, but he happened to be a great businessman for many years and is now doing what he enjoys, which is coaching. He utilizes the four disciplines in his coaching culture. I told you before that I met Coach and Veeola at the same time. He told me many years ago that coaching is how he wanted to spend his time in his sixties," she said.

"So, the fourth discipline is about applying information? Just because I have heard it, read it, or studied it means nothing. Applying the information is what matters. You could have just told me this secret, but without the journey and seeing things in action, I would not know the golden mailbox or mailbox money concept." The lightbulb went off in his head. "Everything seems manageable but also appears to be more work. I already feel like I'm working hard enough and stretched thin. Where will I find time to focus on all this stuff?"

His mentor looked confused. "Let's be real. Before we started our journey, you were coming in the office at nine thirty or ten o'clock in the morning. You were not working as hard as you could have. Success is a choice, young man, so listen to me clearly. Consistent success doesn't happen by accident. I've seen many salesmen score big clients one year, and the next year they are out of the business. This is a journey, a choice first to be successful then to put in the work to get there."

She schooled him further, "In my experience, I have found most of the work from the four disciplines takes place before or after work. People with children, like me, focus on the disciplines after the little ones go to bed, or very early in the morning before the break of day. These crucial hours should be spent on finding ways to build your business instead of playing on your phone. If you enjoy working on your phone, one of my mentors created a tool I can share with you that will help take your business to the next level and keep reminding you about the disciplines. We can talk about that later."

REFLECTION

....

THE SALESMAN LEANED ON the wall, crossed his fingers and put his hands behind his head. "Okay, I'm in! So, what now? Where do I start? I've learned so much on this journey. I understand mailbox money and can see it. I just don't want to forget the disciplines because I know they will help me become better in everything I do." The salesman was ready to act on what he'd learned.

"Okay! Pon atención," she said.

"What did you say?" He questioned.

"Pay attention! You should be an expert by now," she scolded him. "Number one - Stay close to the process of your business. Number two - Visualize your golden mailbox and the line of clients at your mailbox. Number three - Embrace the process of transformation knowing the process will take time. And, number four - Work on enhancing how you receive and convey information in a way that your clients can understand and move them to action." She reminded him. "Apply each of the disciplines to all aspects of your life and think about your mailbox money constantly. Salesman, you think you got this?"

He released a long sigh, "Wooooooooooo! I never stopped to think about my business in this way. I'm really excited to see my golden mailbox grow. I also think this whole journey will make me a better person. I need to get more in touch with the Master of my mailbox as well. That is a whole different conversation I'd love to have with you one day."

She shook her head in agreement. "Yes, I'd like that," she paused. "One more thing. I heard the coach, El Maestro from La Tyme, tell his team this once. There is a plant called the Chinese Bamboo Tree. But, there is an interesting story about this plant. One year after it is planted, you don't see any growth. Nothing at all! Although you don't see it growing, the plant still requires sunlight and water. In years two through four after watering it faithfully, you still don't see any growth. Surprisingly, in the fifth and sixth years, this plant shoots up to seventy-five feet in six weeks. Do you think it was a coincidence that the plant grew so fast, out of nowhere?"

Dumbfounded by the story, the salesman shook his head from side to side.

"In those early years when it appeared that nothing was happening, there was a tremendous amount of activity happening. The activity was not happening on the surface where people could see it. It was happening beneath the soil. The water and sunlight it gained allowed the plant to grow deep roots - roots that would support it when the growth happened. The same is true for your business - your golden mailbox. You may appear to be mastering the disciplines, but your sales numbers may not change immediately. It may feel like you are working harder and more efficient, but the results are the same."

She continued to coach him." Let the disciplines be the water and sunlight your business needs even when you don't see immediate change. While your growth is happening under the soil where no one can see, there may even be some minor failures or doubt. Certain types of failure are surprisingly a great way to grow. Don't be afraid to position yourself where there is a chance to fail. There is a lot that can be gained from failing that can prepare you for the next opportunity."

"By mastering the disciplines, one day your mailbox money will explode out of nowhere and the change will be obvious. Similar to what happens with the Chinese Bamboo tree. Your peers will look at you as you pass them by, and they will wonder what you did. They will wonder what your secret is. They may even ask you to tell them the key. Guard the disciplines as they are not for everyone and can be abused if not learned properly. Many people think they are ready for change, but when it comes down to it, they are not because they do not know the disciplines."

The salesman sat down, closed his eyes, relaxed his hands and the room went silent. The salesman talked to himself in a whisper. "I see Levere. I see Carl. I see Andrea. I see the golden mailbox. I see my line, I see it growing," whispered the salesman. He sat there with eyes closed. He didn't speak for about twenty seconds before he whispered again. "Someone needs me in my line. They have a question. *Yes! I can help you. I'm here!*" He spoke to his vision.

When he opened his eyes, the mentor was looking at him. She smiled at him saying, "Enjoy your day, young salesman! My work is done."

With tears running down his eyes he grabbed a tissue and walked out not wanting her to see him crying. The salesman turned around to look into the glass portion of the door to the mentor's office. He saw her on her knees with her mouth moving, but he couldn't make out what she was saying. The young salesman went to his office, closed the door and fell to his knees giving thanks. As he was on his knees, a group of new recruits were touring the office and looked inside his office. They were amazed at what they saw. The salesman opened his eyes and noticed the recruits. Part of him felt embarrassed and wanted to stand, but he remained on his knees and began to speak in a whisper to himself. "*The journey was long, and I felt confused. But, I did not feel alone. Thank you for answering my prayer when I was in Peru. I asked for some clarity, and you sure gave me all the clarity I can handle. I know my success will not happen based off just my efforts alone. My eyes are open to all those that play a part in my life. I thank you for this journey. All I have is because of you. My golden mailbox and my mailbox money are* because of you."

THE END?

....

WAIT A MINUTE! THERE is more...

The salesman got up and headed back over to the mentor's office. He knocked softly on her door.

The mentor lifted up her head from working on the computer. "Come in," she looked confused when she saw him at her door again. "You're back so soon?"

He nervously fidgeted with his fingers as he spoke, "There is something that I still have a question about."

"What more do you want to know," she questioned. "I've already told you about the golden mailbox and mailbox money, which is what you wanted to know about, right?"

"You did. You told me about the legend of the golden mailbox. But, is there a *real* golden mailbox somewhere? Something tells me there is more."

She looked down at her computer again, then lifted her head to look at him. "Please close the door and sit down," she pulled her chair under as she also sat. "You don't quit, do you?" She smiled as her eye twitched.

To the salesman, she appeared nervous. He hadn't

seen her like that before, so he knew she wasn't telling him everything. "Tell me! Is it out there? Where is it?" He blurted out.

"Yes, the golden mailbox is real. It is in a remote part of the world, and the scrolls of the original disciplines are also there," she shared everything she hadn't shared along the journey. "The tea from Veeola, that helped you with your dream, comes from the mountains where the mailbox is. There are only seven people in the world who know of this. You are now the eighth. You mustn't speak of this with anyone. The others have talked about going on a journey to the mailbox because there have been talks of a fifth discipline that is hidden in the same mountains.

"A fifth discipline? Are you serious?" The salesman jumped out of his seat with excitement. "I just learned the four, and now you are telling me there is potentially more? We must go! There is no way this can be out there, and we don't find it."

The mentor sat in silence and thought for a minute. She picked up the phone to make a call. The salesman listened in on her end of the conversation, "Pack your bags and call the others. We are going for the fifth."

THE END

WORD FROM THE AUTHOR

....

TAKE THE TIME TO read this book over and over for the messages immersed throughout. Each time you read it, you will discover the keys to unlock the techniques to obtaining your own mailbox money.

Visit our website: **www.GlobalMailboxMoney.com** for more resources and tools built around this amazing story. You will never look at your life, your money, your relationships or your mailboxes the same.

Thank you for taking the time out to read Mailbox Money. One last thing the mentor forgot to mention to the salesman that I'd like to share with you is that all who know the legend of the golden mailbox, the energy of the world will now be in your favor. May this energy propel you to greatness!